Down
Half
the World

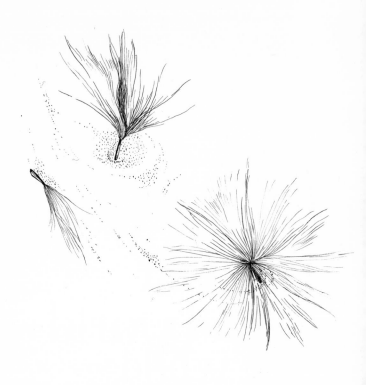

Illustrations by Zena Bernstein

Down
Half
the World

by
Elizabeth Coatsworth

The Macmillan Company, New York
Collier-Macmillan Limited, London

FIRST PRINTING

ACKNOWLEDGMENTS

Many of the poems included in this book first appeared in *Borzoi Battledore*, *The Christian Science Monitor*, *The Dallas Times Herald*, *The Dial*, *Double-Dealer*, *Down East*, *The Forum*, *The Georgia Review*, *The Literary Review* (published by the *New York Evening Post*), *The New-England Galaxy*, *Patterns*, *Poetry*, *Saturday Review*, *Southwest Review*, and *Vanity Fair*.

The poem "Whale at Twilight" appeared originally in *The New Yorker*.

We wish to thank the following for permission to reprint copyrighted material:

Coward-McCann, Inc., for "Daniel Webster's Horses," "The Fates," "The Lady," "A Lady Comes to an Inn," "Night Piece," and "The Ogre Entertains," from *The Creaking Stair*, by Elizabeth Coatsworth, Copyright 1923 by Elizabeth Coatsworth, Copyright 1929, 1949 by Coward-McCann, Inc.; "The Furrows of the Unicorn," "Hang Fu," "Patterns of Life," and "The Windmill Addresses Don Quixote," from *Compass Rose*, by Elizabeth Coatsworth, Copyright 1929 by Coward-McCann, Inc., renewed 1957 by Elizabeth Coatsworth.

Harper & Row, Inc., for "The Infanta," "On the Hills," "Saint John," and "Samson," from *Atlas and Beyond*, Copyright 1924 by Harper & Brothers, renewed 1952 by Elizabeth Coatsworth.

The Estate of Mr. Harold Vinal for "And Laughter Sounded," "Dialogue," "Genesis," "Mary Tudor" (originally entitled "On a Portrait of Mary Tudor in Prado"), "On an Overgrown Hill," "Poem to Hunger," and "Song to Green," all from *Voices*.

Yankee, Inc., for "Body and Spirit," "Fog," and "Sketch for an Island," from *Yankee* magazine. Copyright 1957, 1949, 1949 respectively, by Yankee, Inc.

For Henry, who is always a poet,
whether he writes in verse or prose.

Note

About 1912 the first Imagist anthology was published, presenting a new type of poetry in which the visual image, sharp and clear, was the backbone and reason for writing. Ezra Pound, Amy Lowell, and John Gould Fletcher were among the poets who contributed to it, and the book made a great impact on critics and readers alike. But the wave of new poetry had only begun. Out of the west came Edgar Lee Masters' *Spoon River Anthology* and Carl Sandburg's *Chicago Poems,* while Vachel Lindsay was trading poems for bread as he wandered from farm to farm. In the stir of increasing enthusiasm, Harriet Monroe in Chicago was able to get backing to launch her small monthly magazine, *Poetry,* in which so many famous poets were to appear for the first time. In the east the challenge was taken up. Robert Frost's *North of Boston* appeared; a Maine school girl, Edna St. Vincent Millay, rose to sudden prominence with her *Renascence;* and Harvard was heard from in the early poetry of T. S. Eliot. These were perhaps the leaders, but there were many, many others. They wrote in a great variety of forms, but readers were eager for them all. Perhaps the wise national subconscious recognized the shadow of coming war and set so many birds to singing in the last of the sunlight. There was some debate between school and school, but on the whole Amy Lowell's dictum was accepted: "There is no 'new' poetry, nor 'old' poetry. There are only 'good' and 'bad' poems."

But how many good poems were being written! If they seem less beautiful now, time has dimmed them. But when I first began to write, singing filled the air.

Through all the years, I have gone on writing, still feeling something of that first excitement. I have written in blank verse and written in rhyme. The form has never seemed important. Even when the poems may be shadowed in content, they were written in a mood of exhilaration, always rapidly, with the immediacy of sketches.

What I have tried to catch is the quality of history and of places, sometimes in distant and out-of-the-way countries, but often here in the Maine countryside.

What shall I say? This book is essentially a short record of my delight in the world and in living.

ELIZABETH COATSWORTH

Nobleboro, Maine
February, 1968

Contents

Night Wind
in Spring

Two yellow dandelion shields do not make spring,
nor do the wild duck swimming by the shore,
so self-possessed, so white of side and breast,
nor, I suppose, the change in land-birds' calls,
softened and sweetened to a courting note,
nor the new colors twigs are taking on,
not even the sun which rises early now
and lingers almost until dinner time.
We, too, are valid instruments; we, too, can say
if this be spring or only waning winter.
Tonight the wind is loud about our chimney.
There is no new moon in the sky, nothing but stars:
the Dipper upright on its shining handle,
Sirius bright above a neighbor's house,
and this wind roaming, not enough to scrape
a branch along the roof, or try the shutters
for one to bang. No, just enough to cry
and cry and cry against the stalwart chimney,
as though it were a wanderer who had come
down half the world to find one only door
and that door locked and nothing answering.

Hang Fu

Tick-tock, tick-tock,
goes the clock of the rain in the eaves,
long are the hours of the rain and the moon is hidden,
I would get up, I would put on my robe with silver
   sleeves,
and creeping through a whining door, bridle my horse
   with a silver bridle,
and ride out under the softly dripping leaves.
But the rain holds me in a monotonous net of sound,
tick-tock, tick-tock,
I will to go and I do not will it,
and the opportunity passes as others pass, and the
   hours pass and are drowned,
and the moon will go down and the sun will rise with
   wet locks,
but there will be no mark of my horse in the teeming
   ground.

Birth of
Henri Quatre

This is so brisk, so fine a day,
so sunny and bare, withal so gay
that my memory turns to gallant things,
to the bleak, bright sword that cuts and sings,
to Jeanne d'Albret in her castle at Pau
singing high and singing low,
though her travail be hard and her pain be long
her son shall be born to his mother's song.
I see her lying in the great state bed
with the canopy dark above her head,
two glazed eyes and a rigid mouth
that still sings canticles of the South.
Whatever the pain, she still must sing
for out of cowards, cowards spring,
and the gifts that she holds for her first son are
this night-long song and the realm of Navarre.

When the day is so bleak and wild and gay
my memories turn to Jeanne d'Albret.

Lost Graveyards

In Maine the dead
melt into the forest
like Indians, or, rather,
in Maine the forests shadow round the dead
until the dead are indistinguishably mingled
with trees; while underground,
roots and bones intertwine,
and above earth
the tilted gravestones, lichen-covered, too,
shine faintly out from among pines and birches,
burial stones and trunks
growing together
above the lattices of roots and bones.
Now is the battle over,
the harsh struggle
between man and the forest.
While they lived,
these men and women fought the encroaching trees,
hacked them with axes,
severed them with saws,
burned them in fires,
pushed them back and back
to their last lairs among the shaggy hills,
while the green fields lay tame about the houses.

Living, they fought the wild,
but dead, they rested,
and the wild softly, silently, secretly
returned. In Maine
the dead sooner or later feel the hug of rootlets,
and shadowy branches closing out the sun.

July Storm

Like a tall woman walking across the hayfield,
The rain came slowly, dressed in crystal and the sun,
Rustling along the ground. She stopped at our apple
   tree
Only a whispering moment, then swept darkening
   skirts over the lake
And so serenely climbed the wooded hills.
Was the rainbow a ribbon that she wore?
We never wondered. It seemed a part of her bright-
   ness
And the way she moved lightly but with assurance
   over the earth.

On an Overgrown Hill

If there are ghosts in this house, they should be
  of the sort
through whose ribs one may see the moonlight
as one sees it shine
between these worn-away beams
and through the walls.
It is a frayed gray pattern of a house
held still in place by its great chimney stack.
Who looks at this house sees space more than house:
space frames it, and space fills it, and space shows
through every rent. Who looks at this house sees
the present in relationship to time.
And if he finds life here (say, in the coarse
and orange lilies seething from its doorstep,
making a mat down half the broken terrace)
then any life he finds must be considered
against the field of death. Here all things take
a beauty from their opposites.
Their meaning
is not in themselves. Perhaps never was.

Finder, Please Return
to Henry Thoreau

Where are the hound,
and the red bay horse,
and the dove whose doorway is a cloud?

The lost hound ranges,
the bay horse grazes,
and the dove flies up from the staring crowd.

Lost in the wilderness,
in the mind's forests,
glimpsed by few and caught by none,

the turtledove nests
and, unchained, untethered,
the horse and the hound forever run.

The Horns

The horns! the hunting horns! there's game afoot!
The hounds are baying and the chase sweeps off!

François is in his carriage, too old now
to ride, but not too old to risk his sacred neck
jolting at desperate speed after the hounds.
He likes some lady to risk her neck, too.
Catherine, his daughter-in-law from Italy,
is oftenest with him, a girl in her teens,
a suave, dark girl with tapering, smooth fingers,
who has some reason for disdaining fear.
Here's François, lashing on, madly hallooing,
Catherine, balanced and still, meeting his laughter
with her deliberate smile, and all the court
lathering their mounts hot on the fleeing stag.

The horns! the hunting horns! there's game afoot!
The hounds are baying and the chase sweeps off!

Somewhere ahead, high in her silver saddle,
Diane is riding, Diane dressed all in black,
her face and neck so white they seem to shine
with a cold light against her widow's garments.
Long, slim and delicate, with her high, small breasts

9

she might be Greek Diana come to lead
the hunt among the surging of her hounds
and draw young Henri's heart, as the sea follows
the ever-changing moon.

The horns! the hunting horns! there's game afoot!
The hounds are baying and the chase sweeps off!

Well, to each one the gods give his desire:
François shall see the killing of the stag,
Catherine de' Medici shall be Queen of France
(and though his heir die by Italian poison
François will not believe her implicated),
huntress Diane shall always hear the hoofs
of Henri's horse close-riding on her own,
and he shall hold the moon within his arms.
Old king, young king, mistress, Italian wife,
each shall be satisfied, till Huntsman Death
calls off his pack of years and makes his kill.

The horns! the hunting horns! there's game afoot!
The hounds are baying and the chase sweeps off!

Song to Green

Green is like Time, green creeps, green springs,
green covers over human things:
the broken wall, the arching bone,
the flower pot, the gray headstone,
the road forgotten, hopes and fears,
green laps them all, as do the years.
Green cares not for the works of man,
unnoticed, follows as it can,
filling up footprints, widening cracks,
silently watching at men's backs.
Green never sleeps, green never wakes,
green is the form Time often takes,
green is the measurement of days,
like Time, it heals; like Time, it slays.

Turn of the Night

Now is the hour between midnight and the first false
   dawn
when something troubles the earth as it lies asleep,
and the cock awakes and claps his wings and crows
under the stars, and all the birds which keep
their hidden slumbers among the thickset leaves
awake and chirp for a moment, half in a daze,
and the dog in his kennel stretches, and in the fields
the cattle lurch to their feet and begin to graze.

Now is the turn of the night, the promise of change,
when the troubled mind awakes to take up its care,
but the lover opens his eyes and puts out his hand
through the dark to make certain once more that the
   loved one is there.

Winter Splendor

This is a day to be compared with lions
if one considers the yellow-maned, round-faced sun;
or with an eagle for its icy glare;
or with a stag for something tense and proud
(and perhaps the antlered thickets enter in).
If men were chosen, I'd choose Charlemagne
for what was Northern in him, haughty, clear;
horns would find here their cold and proper echoes;
"magnificent" is perhaps not quite the word
but I can come no nearer. Such a day
towers above its fellows, passing by
with chargers, ermines, pennons, and with spears.

At the
Windowed Horizon

When the rain came which we had seen letting down
  its black hair at the windowed horizon,
it was not rain after all, but hail, white hail,
which fell on the green grass and hopped like little
  frogs;
the east wall drummed at the unexpected touch.
Oh, the fortitude of the robin on her nest in the un-
  protected crotch of the pear tree!
When at last the sun came out, the wet edges of the
  apple leaves winked red,
the hayfield ran emerald down to a pond black as ink
spilled upon paper; the clouds above it were black,
  too, and filled with the rumble of thunder.
Again and again we flung open the front door,
looking for a rainbow, but only the clear cool air
rewarded our eagerness, only the bobolink
sang as he flew, the raindrops shaking from wet wings.

The Telephone
Brought You Back

This morning you were long in answering the telephone.
Were you delayed, coming down the airy stairs of the
towers of sleep?
Or did the subterranean cellars hold you in their darkness
where pot-bellied tuns of wine crowd against one another
and through the rotting partition one hears the hoofs
of the nightmares
restless in their stalls?
Perhaps you were held in the arms of a dream,
your head with its dark bangs and coiling hair
resting on an incorporeal shoulder;
or you may have been wandering in visionary cities
or along nameless highways toward destinations
which veered like weathervanes in every flaw of sleep.
But wherever your spirit may have been,
whatever it was doing or feeling,
the telephone suddenly brought you back,
jerking at you with its tether of sound,
casting in your face the familiar walls, pictures, fur-
niture, window frames,
like a dash of icy water.

The Empresses

Victoria, Carlota, and Eugénie,
were young queens once, were once young empresses,
with ears pierced for their jewels and flower-shaped bon-
    nets
and parasols and billowing bright dresses.

They had young husbands once, with narrow waists
and brave mustaches. They drove satin horses
through shaded parks, and with small smiles presided
at dinners of innumerable courses.

Proud! They were proud, those lovely princesses:
Victoria was determined as a stone,
Eugénie bore the blood of Montezuma,
Carlota gambled for a windy throne.

One won, two lost, all three grew very old,
old women who, before at last they died,
had turned to legends, wearing on their fingers,
like rings, the wars demanded by their pride.

Romanesque Frieze

Louis is leading the crusade from the loftiest of motives,
no one could look at him for a moment and doubt it.
He prays, he fasts, he gives alms, he performs penances.
I swear his war horse has caught the fever and bows his
head every time a priest says amen!
Louis is a dedicated spirit, with the mildness of a nun,
and the courage of a fanatic.
He was well trained by his mother, his blue eyes have
seen a vision,
but Eleanor of Aquitaine, leading her court ladies dressed
as Amazons,
is here in the Holy Land from a most unconsecrated,
unhallowed, unsanctified, itching love of adventure.
She and her squadron are everywhere, interfering with
everything, suggesting a hundred perfectly unfeasible
plans,
scurrying out where they should never have gone on
exploring expeditions,

reclining on silk-spread couches in their pavilions when
    the army should be marching,
discussing the wonders of Constantinople, and the hand-
    someness of its men
while the enemy is ambuscading the rear guard,
mocking the king to his face,
rolling their eyes at the priests, teasing the pages, setting
    the knights to fighting among themselves—
if ever crusading was a mystified and bad business
it is with Eleanor and her court-lady Amazons.
Across all bare and bitter Palestine their forces sweep in
    a comedy of mortality,
she playing an extravaganza of the flesh
beside Louis's extravaganza of the spirit.

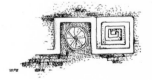

Ensnare the Clouds

It was so still that hour I could see
the morning-glories in the ripened hay
like cool shells gleaming; hurrying down the fields
I found the air pinked with small butterflies,
and at the pond's edge there was only silence,
no smallest lap of ripples, no bird calling,
but silent clouds were floating down the sky
and water lilies floated in the cove,
and I, I swam in whitest cloud reflections
through air that smelled of motionless water lilies.
Once some slight breeze blew a sphered thistledown
along the surface and young dragonflies
in sapphire armor rose from lily pads
to charge the intruder, but the flying thing
unliving, insubstantial, baffled them
and lightly took its wayward course. I followed
and so came to the shore; a green frog watched me
put on my shoes, I sitting on a boulder,
he sitting in the pond, his fingers resting
upon its edge, his golden eyes upon me.
The ocean has its waves, its shells and seaweeds
but ponds have water lilies, ponds ensnare the clouds.

Dialogue

In the monotonous heat
I crave, I desire
to hear a bird sing.
Heart, old heart,
have you a bird that will sing
deep among the browning leaves?

In the monotonous heat
I crave, I desire
the coolness of a spring.
 Heart, old heart,
is there still a spring
among dry boulders in the late sun?

In the montonous heat
I crave, I desire
a wind at close of day.
I long for a horse
without saddle, without bridle,
to carry me away.

There is such a bird, such a spring,
such a wind, such a horse,
I heard my heart say.

And Were
a Little Changed

Don't look in the engagement calendar for memories:
not whom you met, nor what was said, nor done, nor eaten
can count among the ashes of time, but only something
(probably unlooked for) something which came out of
    space
and passed you as it went its way, and you stopped and
    looked
and were a little changed. That is your history.
A storm was coming, the light became the storm light
and we were on the river going against the tide
gray-green with the light across it. It was cold
and the wind was blowing. At the head of a narrow island
a great concourse of sea gulls and cormorants had gathered,
they flew upward, unraveling upward from the water.
The gulls were bone-white, the cormorants black as soot
against the storm clouds, and the swirling gulls
rose high and light, while the dark cormorants
splattered the water with their feet.
They were like spirits, good and evil angels
gathered above the dying; souls, not fish,
one felt, in a great shoal going upriver,
souls and not fish the birds were noisy over,
their wings against the clouds and spruce-dark hillsides.

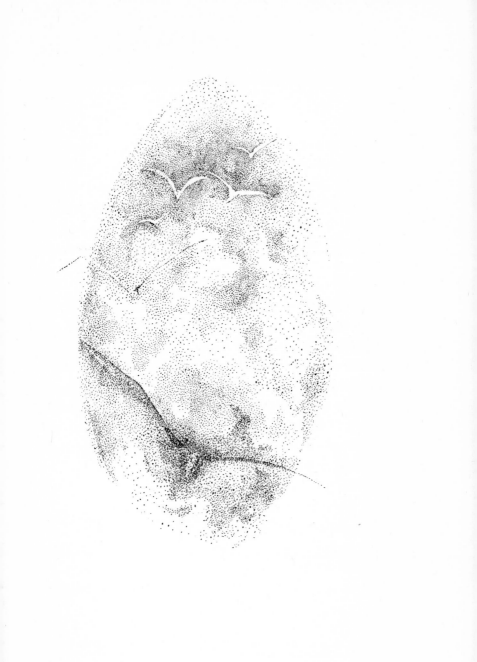

Patterns of Life

Our little boat
swung by, close to the lumber schooner
almost in the shadow of her gray sails.
In the heat a man was lying along the rail
with a bare mellow back and old duck trousers,
motionless, absorbed in the ripples,
absorbed in the heat like a lizard.
At the wheel a thin man was standing,
chewing tobacco, one foot on the taffrail.
He gave us a shrewd look and raised a hand to us.
How many beautiful patterns of life there are, I thought,
and we can live only one and often that is not beautiful—
oh, is any one of them always beautiful from the inside?
And the white shadow of our sail disengaged itself from
   gray shadows
and the chug-chug of auxiliary engines grew fainter and
   fainter in our ears.

Whale
at Twilight

The sea is enormous, but calm with evening and sunset,
rearranging its islands for the night, changing its ocean
  blues,
smoothing itself against the reefs, without playfulness,
  without thought.
No stars are out, only sea birds flying to distant reefs.
No vessels intrude, no lobstermen haul their pots,
only somewhere out toward the horizon a thin column of
  water appears
and disappears again, and then rises once more,
tranquil as a fountain in a garden where no wind blows.

Columbus
and the Mermaids

Off the coast of Hispaniola
off the strange coast, returning,
   the *Santa Maria* sighted three manatee,
sea cows holding their calves in their flippers
   above the water, suckling their young,
staring at the great sails
   and the high decks
and the ornate carvings of the *Santa Maria*
   with dark, round, unenlightened eyes.

And at the three manatee
   the Spaniards, saturated with wonders,
stared back, wondering still.
   Here were the sea women, the mermaids of whom
      men told,
the ones who combed their hair with golden combs,
   and sang ships to the rocks. Fishermen had caught
such in their nets and dragged them home
   weeping their pearl-like tears.

They had christened and even married them
    and begot children by them, children with green eyes.

Here were these wonders, yet like other wonders,
    once grappled, these seemed less than wonderful,
and that great dreamer, writing the ship's log,
    Columbus, thoughtful, turning the quill between
long fingers, meditating, frowning a little,
    possibly realizing that nothing is what it seems
(even islands, even continents), wrote of his mermaids:
    "They are not so beautiful as they are painted."

Earth and
the Kisses of Men

The peasants of Calabria,
receiving at last the land
which they and their fathers
from earliest times have tended,
kneel down, they say,
to kiss the half-starved,
fever-shaken earth of their mother,
their bearded lips
tender upon the hot, eroded soil.

Oh earth, earth, do you treasure
the kisses of men?
The desperate, passionate kisses
of explorers, kneeling on beaches,
their swords in their hands?
With a kiss they have greeted new continents,
their full lips
have touched the earth on which their armored feet
and the shod hoofs of their horses
were to echo.

Always with the fear, with the greed,
with the uncertainty, with the pride,
there has been love.

Before their hands
have stripped a land of its wealth
their lips have touched it.
For that moment,
joy has swept through them,
they have been shaken
by humbleness and wonder.

But the seas
have sent their storms,
and wiped away the place.
The clouds
have rained their torrents,
and wiped away the place.
The winds
have loosed their strengths,
and blown away the place.
What sand, what earth, on island, or on main,
can say "Columbus touched me with his lips"?
"Here Cortez knelt"? or "Champlain's kiss fell here"?

Fog

Waking, I knew the sea had come again.
I knew the crying sea gull winging by
the long, long roll of fog above our roof,
as truly of the sea as though a breaker
had swept inland and covered all the woods,
the fields, the hollow ponds with its vast height
of living water; this was only air
but whitened, laden with the smell of the sea
and with sea dampness. At my side the ghost
laid a chill finger on my lip and breathed
its silence into me, and I lay in silence
unstirring, drowned, with all my hair in tendrils.

Heavy
Is the Heat

Heavy is the heat, heavy and solid
as a cloak of gold, as a hood of gold,
as shoes of gold, as bracelets of gold,
weighing down the shoulders, weighing down the head.
The feet are weary and the hands move slowly
and the heart remembers the cold.

In their hot caverns among the leaves
the birds are silent or utter peevish cries.
The flowers droop on their stems, the dust falls back to
   the road
when a car passes, cows seek the shadows,
the dogs lie panting on the steps, the cats have vanished,
and even green oppresses the heavy, slow-moving eyes.

Les Isles d'Amérique

So far from Fontainebleau those islands lay,
so far from Paris and its palaces!
They were less real than those of Cythera,
they were chimeras such as lovers dream
watching the archipelagoes of the clouds
in a blue sky. So far those islands lay
that vessels bound for them must be provisioned
as for a siege, and brought back curious tales
of heats, and fruits, and storms that beat like drums,
and huge black savages singing in the fields,
and governors, sitting at meat with pirates,
whose dark ships lay and laughed safe in the harbors.
So far from Paris, so far from Fontainebleau
lay those lush islands of America!

Under their trees were darkness and crushed fruit,
and snakes that coiled. From their mysterious harbors
sailed hogsheads of strong rum, and cones of sugar
made from crushed cane, distilled with oxen's blood.
Against black breasts the planters' children slept
and for their lullabies had incantations,
nursed by enslaved African sorceresses.

What star burned bright over the roofs of Paris,
what meteor fell over green Fontainebleau
when Françoise d'Aubigné (called Maintenon)
Was born in those far islands?
Did a wind
Blow through Versailles heralding Josephine?

Mary Tudor

I have seen
a portrait of this Mary,
this thin queen
with anxious eyes and narrow tight-sealed lips,
holding a rose in her sharp finger tips.
She has done what she can in hopes to please
her Spanish king lagging across the seas.
Has she not given him her withered heart,
that fiery pinch of dust? Is not her will
limp in his hand? Philip has but to ask
and Mary, Queen of England, must fulfill.
She woos him with a parchment tenderness,
her dangerous sister at his word she spares,
and with the executioner's sword and hempen rope
from English blood a love knot she prepares,
and sends this portrait where one reads the pains
of Tudor blood turned acid in the veins.

Johnsonia

The old doctor has at last retired to his room,
but not yet to his bed and the visions that torment him.
Above the candle it is his great face that is hanging,
and the room is filled with the smell of his wig, singeing
   unnoticed.
It is three o'clock. Mrs. Thrale has made him his tea,
but no protests nor wisdom nor wit could keep her up
   longer.
There is no one to talk to. The ponderous, intricate mind
is left to itself and its own overmastering fears.
All around him are darkness and night, but old Doctor
   Johnson
will not yield for a while. He has made for himself a
   bulwark
of a book and a candle, and there will he sit for hours
forlorn, with his singeing wig—he whom all London
   fears!

Birthday Party

Beneath the high solemn dusk of Westminster
what is this little bustle, these smothered giggles among
   the tombs,
this petty flouncing of skirts and wagging of coattails
in the vast emptiness of death?
Who should it be but Samuel Pepys, gentleman,
with his wife and her servant (who sings to the flute)
and his boy (who knows how to dance)
and Bob and Betty, his cousins from the country,
all peering and screeching at the body of Queen Catherine of Valois,
shown here for a shilling, as a special favor?
Samuel Pepys is thirty-six years old today. It is an occasion.
He turns back his ruffles. He even touches the mummy.
The cousins squawk, his French wife takes to her smelling
   salts,
the maid cries, "La! sir, you never would!"
In a pleasing stir and bustle, summoning his courage,
Mr. Pepys of the Admiralty leans over and pecks the dry
   black mouth of the body.

What a man with the ladies, to be sure! But by all
means, let us get into the sunshine!

Faugh! how cold the place is! what a smell there is of
death!

He packs them into the hackney coach. "That's what all
your fine wenches and madams must come to!"

Shrills Mrs. Pepys, head out of the window, yet even her
hungry jealousy never guessing

that Mr. Samuel Pepys is walking on a pavement of
dreams

with the touch of a queen's mouth on his lips.

Winter Thaw

Against the moon the icicles hang black.
Uneven fangs they seem, so sinister
yet meaningless; the north wind having changed
they too are changing, drip and drip and drip,
they wear, like time, away, and make a small
reiterated song or perhaps complaint
as meaningless as their fierce hungry look
seeming to seize the moon, yet seizing nothing.

Split the Stones

The roots of trees go everywhere
nor speak of what they find,
most innocent of tentacles,
most innocent and blind.

They crack the coffin like a nut,
split stones and wrap around
the miser's strongbox buried once
in what was barren ground.

Confessor-secret, lawyer-sly
they tell not where they've been
nor why the branches are so thick,
nor what makes leaves so green.

The Cabin

There were no windows in the cabin, and the door
hung twisted in the door frame; there was no bed
to call a bed, only a bench of boards
on which old leaves were heaped; the hearth had fire
but there was nothing to be cooked there, nothing.
The woman dragging through her work was hungry
and could give nothing to her hungry child.
No voice came but the wind's voice, scrape of branches
against the leaking roof, the cold insistence
of February wind at the warped door.
The man was elsewhere, since the lair he'd made
was not much to his taste, his wife too listless
to laugh at tavern stories, and the time
nearing responsibility. The man was gone
but night was there, the wind was there, and pain—
they were the midwives that the woman had
until a neighbor happened by. In so far
the baby had a human birth, not further.
Then to him lying between thin arm and breast
came the dread godmothers: poverty, shiftlessness,
the wandering fever, ignorance, and dirt,
hopelessness, hunger, and a deep despair,
each stood beside him, touched him on the brow.

The mother sighed and drew the torn quilts closer,
the February wind clapped at the door,
flattening the fire on the careless hearth.
Then came another, dark and wrapped in darkness,
the spirit of that earth, by none expected.
She stood among the hags, who left the child
with lingering looks. Fiercely she caught him up,
stared in his eyes, laid her great face to his
and held him close, taking him for her own.
The sleeping mother gave an uncertain smile
as though she heard a voice that seemed to bring
good news in speech she did not understand;
and somewhere someone said to Thomas Lincoln,
"I guess your wife's got a surprise to home.
You pay for drinks. Your Nancy's borned a boy."

March
in New Mexico

1

Coming home in the cold wind,
coming home through the sudden snow,
I thought, What if the fruit trees are not in blossom?
What if the birds have not yet come?
There is something inside me which is in blossom.
There is something inside me which lifts its head.

2

Walking with the Black Mesa beside me,
I said, I am glad that the mountains are hidden.
The clouds are low: we see only the hems of their gar-
    ments,
patterned with snow. I am glad they are hidden.
Walking with the Black Mesa beside me
I said, It is better to feel the mountains very high,
very high and white behind the cloud banks.

3

The little horse is galloping. Quick, quick, he carries his
   rider.
They are going to the house of a girl,
the girl who lives by the river.
See how deep the hoofs cut into the sand!
See how close the hoof prints lie together!
The trail is a love poem, a little stanza which the desert
   wind will erase.

A Wind Blows

Only in the wilderness where no man may live,
nor the works of his hands survive,
can a man take the measure of man,
weigh him against the blowing sands,
tally his shadow in the blaze of the sun,
and untangle his words from the daggers of the thorn
bushes.
There shall a man see the sudden flower growing
from the scapegoat's whitened ribs;
water trickles over the salt sand,
and overhead, like a thin-drawn eye,
the hawk hangs, mewing.
Man is a stranger in the wilderness,
his measures are lost, he is housed in indifference,
silence stares into his face,
terror communes with him,
nothingness looks over his shoulder.
After such companionship, if he return at all,
he returns speaking strange words:
a wind blows through his thoughts,
and, raising a gaunt forearm,
he prophesies.

In the Late Afternoon

What were her thoughts, the woman, Bathsheba,
who had bathed away her husband's life in the delicious
   cool of the late afternoon
amid the crying of swallows?
What were his thoughts, he who had sat on his roof
troubled by his hot palace, the war, his turbulent people,
running thick shepherd fingers through a regal beard
and gazing over his city with unappeased eyes?
Below the palace roof the other roofs spread out, flat,
   dull gold,
in endless patterns of intersecting squares cut by narrow
   gulfs of shadow.
The light slanted across the dusty air; a few vendors
   cried their goods,
and a woman bathed herself in a little pool that changed
   with the sky.
That night the blazing sun sank deeper and deeper into
   the heart of the king,
and Bathsheba, standing pensively above the circle of
   crimson-bright water,
shone copper as the hilt of a Philistine poniard upright
   in a wound.

Saint John

A wild pleasure for Saint John
in the desert wandering,
under red cliffs pondering,
shaggy-headed, facing dawn,
stooping at lost pools to drink,
meditating by their brink,
stripping fruit from desert trees,
stealing honey from the fierce small bees . . .

A wild pleasure for Saint John
visionary, swift and thin,
wrapped about by a goat's skin
(nothing man had worked or woman
woven), like a hairy beast
curled in a beast's den to rest,
dreaming with a saint's elation
of the terrible and lonely pathway to salvation . . .

A wild pleasure for Saint John
in a blinding recognition
to have known his Lord and mission,
from the desert to have gone,
shrilling great outrageous things
in the angry ears of kings,
till that head from desert sands
a princess, hot with dancing, carried between her hands.

The Windmill
Addresses Don Quixote

My honored sir, before you pick yourself
up from the ground to mount that curious horse,
let us speak calmly. There was no ill feeling
on my part in the whole affair:
I but pursued my course.
Your fault is always to see personalities
in everything, even a cosmic force.

And could you not have looked behind appearances
and seen that brandished arms may lead to bread?
This obstinate rushing at surface characteristics
does credit to your heart:
not to your head.
Believe me, properly taken, my vans are more useful
than that Dulcinea's fan, of whom you've read.

Meditation at Elsinore

"Good night, sweet prince"—
That is the tragedy,
not blood, not poison,
not even the reedy stream
where flowers and little bawdy ditties ended.
The tragedy was love.
Love was the chord to which the young prince moved,
and one by one his loves betrayed his love:
his father's ghost was harsh and stank of Hell;
his mother's love was coupled with the siren's;
while young Ophelia spoke, her father listened;
his boon companions came as spies;
on every hand
his love turned sword and twisted in his grasp,
piercing his side. But others died as well.
Despite this heaped-up death, these corpses strewn
as thick as daisies in a meadow, hate
was never victor. All was done for love;
not hate, but love speaks last—
"Good night, sweet prince."

Samson

You need not pity Samson,
he was one
to like his honey ripped from lions' bellies,
sweetness was stale that did not smell of death.
Unless a woman were made dangerous
with latent treachery, silkier than her hair,
she was not worth his boisterous attention.
He liked to pile the odds against himself
and then at the last moment turn the tables,
roaring his sinister jests above his victims.
He understood the path Delilah followed,
played with himself and her, experimental
as always at the lip of a volcano.
Well, he was singed, and felt the smart awhile,
but had a death completely to his taste:
jeers turned to screams had always been his music,
festivals clinched with blood tickled his humor.
You need not pity Samson,
he was one
to like his honey ripped from lions' bellies.

Poem to Hunger

It is Hunger who says to the gull
"Fly up, stretch those wide wings,
search, search along the margins of the tide,"
and rouses the black crow with the same cry
by which she once drove dragons from their lairs.
Now the fox
wakens to stretch and put a light foot forth
into the snow. The green tides of the sea
are not so deep, so covered with the wings
of storms, but that the deathless voice can find
a way into the furthest cave. The coiling snake
is earless as he lies in the warm sun
and Hunger calls and he lies staring out
motionless it may be for hours or days,
yet in the end he heeds, as all must heed:
each must go out, each take his appointed good
dark with the shadow of death.
The nest, the den, the fissure of the rock,
the shadow of the leaf close to the stem,
the little burrow scooped with desperate claws:
all shelters must be emptied, all deserted
when Hunger shouts, if she shout loud enough.
Remember that, weak heart. There is no hiding.
Only the skeleton lies with bones unstirring,
only the dead man never leaves his fastness
for the unknown, by which the living live.

Yet the
Lean Beast Plays

Man lives by his sweat but the bird works harder
for his food is locked in a difficult larder,
and the rabbit lives at the skirts of death,
and the fox draws many a starving breath,
and the great hawk coasting the cloudy sky
stares down from a proud but ravenous eye.
The tight belt of hunger, the necklace of fear,
alas! one beholds them everywhere.
Yet the lean beast plays, and the song goes up,
and honey is sweet in the bitter cup,
and love makes a music ever its own
though the lyre be strung on a hollow bone.

The Furrows
of the Unicorn*

The furrows of the unicorn are crooked,
they straggle anyhow
where the frail beast has plunged in the loam's blackness
bound to the plow,
striving and struggling on with sides bemired
and silver-hornèd brow.

The furrows of the unicorn are crooked,
ragged as pain,
his life in arrased forests teaches nothing
of bit and rein,
and where his hoofs have staggered down the meadow
springs blood-red grain.

* Canst thou bind the unicorn with his band in the furrow? or will he
harrow the valleys after thee?—Job 39:10

The Three Deer

Between the full moon and the hoarfrost
(the smooth white and the shaggy)
dark stood three deer under dark apple boughs.
Rounded were they as pebbles and as easeful,
nothing they feared and nothing they endangered.
The morning star had not paled in the east,
the lattices of night were not yet opened to the dawn.
Deer and the watcher at the window shared one stillness
between full moon and hoarfrost in that eddy of time.

Genesis

Oh, what a pleasure for the animals
at last to pass before the eyes of Adam
and at his words discover what they were.
The tender-eyed giraffe among the thickets
knew himself as giraffe; the lion flaunted
his mane with a new pride; the elephant
raised high his trunk and bugled a salute;
the peacock spread his tail to play the peacock;
the white doves preened and cooed: the myriads
of creatures, birds, and crawling things of earth
at last were differentiated by a name.
There Adam lolled beneath the breath of God
and out of formlessness brought form to being,
building with words a world of consciousness.
His first experience was to mark him artist
and only after that exhilaration
fell that long slumber, out of which rose Eve.

The Long Black Grave

How goes it, turtle?
    Ill. Stupid and slow
    I did not guess which way to go.
    Now I shall never reach the place toward which some
        instinct pulled me.

And, cat?
    I, the night-hunter,
    in shattering brightness became the hunted.
    The eyes undid me. Here I lie.

And you, snake?
    It seemed a hard glade between grass and grass,
    but one I could not pass.

Bird, what, you, too?
    The beetle, night-chilled, warmed itself and I
    stooped down with folded wings.
    They are wide open now
    but never more will fly.

You, little frogs?
    We danced, high-hopping in the evening rain
    who will not leap again.

So many skunks?
  Our hearts fear nothing.
  For neither great nor small
  will we give way.
  We did not.
  That is all.

Raccoons, opossums, now and then, a dog?
  We knew the danger
  as men know it, yet
  we, too, like men, thinking of other things, forget.
  Here where we died, we lie,
  hair, flattened bone,
  forfeit to speed
  which swallowed up our own.

Insect, bird, beast, and snake,
my heart is heavy for your sake.
The tomb of Rameses was hid
within a towering pyramid.
Your graves are the long roads that run
from rising sun to setting sun.

Harmony

I being silent, the woods began to sing,
the dark woods and the long white slopes of snow.
The cold blue sky joined with them and the wind
blowing from the northwest, blowing the smoke
from far-spaced chimneys. All the country sang.
There was no need of bird-song nor of mine.
It did not matter to the lonely north
if there were listeners or if there were none.
The song was there, the singers once more met
as they had met together, long and long.
Only a cloud could change the song they sang,
only a cloud, or darkness slowly rising
out of the east, among the brightening stars.

At Twilight

At twilight
we are all
at twilight
we are
at twilight
we are all orphans.

As the light fades
our confidence
as the light fades
our assurance
fades.

The moon in the eastern sky
even the moon
serene as a nursemaid
does not
even the moon
cannot
wipe away the tears
the tears
we do not know
we shed.

A Lady
Comes to an Inn

Three strange men came to the inn.
One was a black man, pocked and thin,
one was brown with a silver knife,
and one brought with him a beautiful wife.

That lovely woman had hair as pale
as French champagne or finest ale,
that lovely woman was long and slim
as a young white birch or a maple limb.

Her face was like cream, her mouth was a rose,
what language she spoke nobody knows,
but sometimes she'd scream like a cockatoo
and swear wonderful oaths that nobody knew.

Her great silk skirts like a silver bell
down to her little bronze slippers fell,
and her low-cut gown showed a dove on its nest
in blue tattooing across her breast.

Nobody learned the lady's name,
nor the marvelous land from which she came,
but still they tell through the countryside
the tale of those men and that beautiful bride.

Night Piece

What I know
no one dreams.
The wind that night
covered all screams.

The moon preferred
to mantle her head.
The cook and butler
were long in bed.

I could not sleep,
the wind was so loud;
a white eye glared
from a tattered cloud;

I could not sleep;
I went down the hall;
I never moved;
I saw it all.

No one shall ever
know what took place.
The moon held a darkness
over her face.

The wind shrieked loud
like a passing spirit.
I shall say nothing.
I inherit.

Song
of the Earth

The times are sad,
but Earth has known
sadness as seasonal as winter.

Death's footsteps
echoing down her paths
will not, after these eons, grieve her.

She drinks all sadness
in like rain
to her deep fountains and dark springs.

Her violets
and primroses
are rooted in lost sorrowings.

Now
in the Stillness

Now in the stillness and the aloneness
the blossom returns to the tree,
and the bird to its nest,

the light returns to the water,
the shadow to the boulder,
and I return to myself.

But No

I am not an old China hand,
but by now I should at least be an old hand at living,
able to give the low-down on the native population,
what a young person may hope for from the human race,
and again, never take for granted; some of the tricks, the
    malices
one will encounter; the dangers darkening the alleys;
the way, too, to the Monday market of kindnesses,
and behind what gate lies the Garden of Content,
and in what coin the gatekeeper is to be paid.
I should be able to give directions to the pavilion in
    which I have so often sat
overlooking the pool, with its bird-filled willow trees.
Possibly, possibly.
But I never fully understood the weather
nor from what quarter the winds blew which lashed the
    pool blind,
silenced the birds, and brought with them the rains,
broken twigs, muddied paths and a hurried retreat
past the guardian dogs and out into the street.

The Ogre Entertains

I, guest to ogres, naturally understand
an ogre's castle must be built on bones
however mortised. There can be no smoke
from homesteads rising on a demon's land.
The servants have a way of snuffing out
and sometimes I have heard when all alone
a sighing from the pillars,
a mural groan.

I walk among the gardens.
Do not think
I cannot guess what once the statues were
that languish in the hedge, and I infer
the origin of the deer from their sad eyes.
I trail my gown along the formal walks
and in the trees above me hear the cries
of clip-winged birds. I do not pick a rose
for fear of wounded stalks.

And night by night I lie in my plumed bed
lulled to slow sleep
by the monotonous, the heavy creep
of the old ogre pacing overhead.

The Lady

The candle is out,
it has crashed to the floor,
she follows the wall
to find the door.

Her petticoats hiss
with a hiss of fear,
a pathway of sound
for a sensitive ear.

When she puts out her hand,
her breath gives a catch,
fingers are there
instead of a latch.

When she reaches back
lest she should fall,
a body is there
instead of a wall.

What use to scream
so sole alone,
what use to struggle
against the unknown?

"Very well," she said
imperiously,
"pray light the sconces
so we may see.

"Here are my pearls,
and here my rings,
and take off your hats,
you filthy things!"

On the Hills

Today I walked on lion-colored hills
with only cypresses for company,
until the sunset caught me, turned the brush
to copper,
set the clouds
to one great roof of flame
above the earth,
so that I walked through fire, beneath fire,
and all in beauty.
Being alone
I could not be alone, but felt
(closer than flesh) the presences of those
who once had burned in such transfigurations.
My happiness ran through the centuries
and linked itself to other happiness
in one continual brightness. Looking down,
I saw the earth beneath me like a rose
petaled with mountains,
fragrant with deep peace.

Sketch
for an Island

This patch of land, these stones, this grass,
and parchment-wearing trees
(not twice the height of any man),
like the Hesperides
yet make an island; water flows,
you see, on either hand,
split by this modest eminence,
divided from the land.

Although the eyes from passing trains
with one indifferent glance
may sweep it all: still it remains
an acre of romance.
No island ever was so mean,
its foliage so thin
but that the bird of fancy flies
to build her nest therein.

The Infanta

Blazoned upon the shadows in her stiff gorgeousness,
one hand upon her boarhound's heavy collar,
the other on the shoulder of her dwarf,
the Infanta walks among her flowers.

As she passes they seem to hold themselves like courtiers,
brightly at attention. The fountains bow before her weary
    eyes,
the black cypresses murmur obsequiously,
everything grows hieratic at her coming,
even the toad she startles by the hedges
seems to hop pompous as a chamberlain.

Wearily the pale blue eyes of the Infanta
wander through the trimmed magnificence of her roses,
gently, as though reading from an unseen document,
she praises them.

Women of Syracuse

Daintily the women of Syracuse
hold their perfume bottles to their noses
and peer down into the quarries.

They are fine women to look at
with eyes that can pick out a sail among running breakers,
knowing as well as the men all the good points of a horse,
why such a team failed at the Olympic games
and such another won by a chariot length,
trained also in poetry and drama, with a provincial en-
    thusiasm,
and showing a tendency to play the grand lady,
be carried hither and thither in their litters,
school their strong hill-born limbs to a pretended languor
and force themselves to faint upon occasion.

Daintily the women of Syracuse
hold their perfume bottles to their noses
and peer down into the quarries.

A great many of the prisoners are still alive—
those over there are probably only sleeping,
the dead they seem to have piled up together.

The keen clear eyes of the Syracusan women
take in the details, how the men hold themselves,
what elegance they show even in starving.
To the Athenians, they in turn seem goddesses
against the sky above the quarry walls.
The tall poised women infinitely far
arouse their pride; they do not ask for pity:
it is enough they have an audience
to whom to play their final act of death.

Daintily the women of Syracuse
hold their perfume bottles to their noses
and peer down into the quarries.

The Bourbons
at Naples

They will refuse you consideration,
they will refuse you privacy, decency,
so much as paper to write on, a book to read,
you will be bruised by their blank indifference.

They will refuse you the sight of any friend,
and of the sun and the moon and the stars,
the wind even and the rain.
They will refuse you wine and meat,
they will refuse you poison.

A hearing, too, they will refuse you.
Stone ears will listen, stone eyes look,
stone fingers scribble, scribble.
They will refuse you mercy,
justice you will be refused.

They will refuse you absolution,
they will refuse you priest and candle,
and the words of comfort before the dawn.
No consolation shall come near you.
In life they will refuse you everything
and after—
they will refuse God your soul.
They will refuse me your body.

This Is a Night

This is a night on which to pity cats
hunting through dripping hedgerows,
making wet way
through grasses heavy with rain,
their delicate stepping
tense with distaste,
their soft and supple coats
sodden, for all their care.
This is a night
to pity cats which have no house to go to,
no stove, no saucer of milk, no lowered hand
sleeking a head, no voice to say, "Poor kitty."
This is a night
on which to weep for outcasts, for all those
who know the rain but do not know the shelter.

The Fates

The Fates,
like hooded hawks
upon God's glove,
often shake their bells
before striking.

Body and Spirit

The body keeps an accurate count of years.
They are like fagots, laid upon its back,
which it must carry down a darkening road
to an unlighted house.
But the bold spirit
pays little heed to time. If it grow weary
it is through sorrow, not through age. It looks
daily upon its image in the glass
with a surprised contempt. What is this creature?
This is a glove that does not fit my hand.

From Cadillac Mountain

So might a Chinese sage have seen the world,
seen mist and humpbacked islands from a mountain,
with a hawk hanging in a silver sky.
So might a Chinese sage have seen his heart
and its tranquility shown in elements

of earth, sky, water, the only fire
white fire of the sun. Here the wind
has come from far away, unhurriedly
traveling from plains and forests, nameless lakes
to seek the ocean and new hemispheres.
The mind, stiffened with routine, stretches, floats
off with the mist, off with the quiet wind
to undefined horizons of its own.

Dedicated
to Her Highness

The Queen of Sheba was a true romantic.
Her imagination being touched, she prepared a caravan,
marshaled her servants, loaded her dromedaries
with spices and gold,
and with precious stones,
and so set off, a queen leaving her kingdom
to follow an adventure of the mind.
Paltry-spirited persons, remembering Solomon's known
  tendencies,
and thinking that as she admired him
she must have loved him,
have underestimated the quest,
and deduced from it the entire line of the Abyssinian
  kings.
But her first interest in him was intellectual.
She weighed relentlessly the profundity of his mind
with questions she had evolved in the long days of medi-
  tation
on her swaying dromedary
among the noises and confusions of the march.
It was the story of his wisdom that had stirred her in her
  kingdom,
it was to test it that she had made her dangerous way-
  faring.

His prosperity, and his house built from the cedars of
  Lebanon
with its throne flanked by golden lions and its shields of
  gold,
his stables and his chariots, the pillars embossed with
  lilies and pomegranates,
the numbers of his servants and the orderliness of his
  household—
these things proved to her that from understanding comes
  peace,
and from peace, beauty. They were the justifications of
  knowledge.
So, having found the truth of travelers' tales,
she gave praise with the warm courtesy of a queen,
presented and received gifts as was the custom,
and took her departure once more into the mythical
  depths of Sheba,
a sovereign in state, surrounded by her servants.

Moses

Plainly then, he was a desert man,
the thing they call a pathfinder: violent, generous,
sowing what others reap, discovering lands
for others to inherit. There have been many
brought up in luxury who have found themselves
at odds with their societies and departed
into the wilderness somewhat less spectacularly,
but who have also struck water from obstinate rock,
communed with visions, boldly made the law
with their own hands, and set their twi-horned foreheads
against all difficulties. There have been others
who once were leaders, yet lie in unmarked graves.

And Laughter Sounded

It may not be Saint Anthony hated devils
as much as he imagined and reported,
living with an horizon circumscribed
by dark cave walls and a burnt strip of desert,
with nothing but the highly codified virtues
of God to think about, and little pastime
but flagellations, and fasts for occupation—
in such a state, austere but very dull,
the massed incursion of a horde of demons
(small rogues blowing upon a nose for hornpipe,
dancing on sword blades, tweaking feathered ears,
trundling egg-bodies, squeaking, squealing, singing,
filling the cavern with their jollity)—
in such a state such an incursion coming
must have been relished even by a hermit,
a white-brow-twitching, skull-stoop-shouldered saint,
let alone visitations of a gentler sort
when human-seeming fingers caught his rosary
and laughter sounded in and out his prayers.

Daniel Webster's Horses

If when the wind blows
rattling the trees,
clicking like skeletons'
elbows and knees,

you hear along the road
three horses pass,
do not go near the dark
cold window-glass.

If when the first snow lies
whiter than bones,
you see the mark of hoofs
cut to the stones,

hoofs of three horses
going abreast—
turn about, turn about,
a closed door is best!

Upright in the earth
under the sod
they buried three horses,
bridled and shod,

Daniel Webster's horses—
he said as he grew old:
"Flesh, I loved riding,
shall I not love it, cold?

"Shall I not love to ride
bone astride bone,
when the cold wind blows
and snow covers stone?

"Bury them on their feet
with bridle and bit.
They were good horses,
see their shoes fit."

Keep Away

The lake
ruffles its gray feathers
and snaps a hawk beak.
Keep away!
There is death in its transparent eye,
those who are gripped by its cold talons
are slow to rise again to the winter sun.
The ice will form a white roof;
dark with ooze is the floor,
and secret and silent are the inhabitants of that house.
No cockcrow will ever waken a sleeper
from that deep bed.
The sun cannot lay a hand on his shoulder:
get going, boy, it's time to be up;
the moon can never rest her cheek against his,
nor the wind ruffle his hair with casual kindness.
And when at last spring opens the door, so long closed,
the guest at that inn, who comes to the doorstep,
is greeted with terror and with tears.

Day Moon

Across the sparkling snowfields and the dark pines
they confront one another in a cloudless sky,
the sun and moon. He stands, triumphant, clothed with
    light,
she is the intruder, pale but self-possessed.
If this is not her hour, not her place,
she shows no vulgar lack of confidence
and having come,
clearly she will remain.

Fly

A fly buzzes up the pane,
climbs, struggles, falls again,
for a little time is still
flattened on the window sill
then begins it all again
buzzing up the windowpane,
gains its height, tries to hold,
then falls back as of old,
to flatten on the window sill
and for a little time lie still
before it gathers strength again
to struggle up the windowpane
and almost gain the top, not quite,
it slips and buzzes from the height,
defeated on the window sill
to lie a little, small and still,
before it tries again to gain

its goal on the smooth windowpane,
where it will slip, where it will fall
repeating, like a nightmare, all
its journey to the window sill
where it will lie, exhausted, still,
and then will gather strength again
to struggle up the windowpane,
to struggle to the slippery crown
and weakly buzzing, thence slip down
until—*I* cut the sequence short.
Life does not haste to spoil the sport—
at last the fly lies very still
and dies upon the windowsill.

Conversation
by Loch Ness

"Monster, with the head of a horse,
what are you, troubling quiet waters?"
"I am the unknown.
I live under all quiet waters.
I am the thing beyond your calculations,
below them,
above them,
alone.
I come from an earlier era of the earth and sea,
and live close and deep.
You will dream of me in your sleep.
Explain me away if you can,
you will not be rid of me."

"Monster, with the maned neck of a snake,
rippling the quiet water without waves,
such creatures as you we have seen
in carboniferous graves.
Your race is long extinct."
"Yet am I here.
The past lives on when you least acknowledge it,
lives on below the surface
in the depths below quiet waters.
You will see it back of your sons' clear eyes,
behind the smiles of your daughters."

Aux Tuileries 1790

The queen only embroiders. She cannot read
with such a brood of terrors in her heart.
Her mind beats hither and thither while she sits
outwardly calm, her heavy-lidded eyes
fixed on the silks her hands are busied with.
Up, down, the needle like a little dagger
strikes to its mark and carries its bright thread
true to the pattern. She can untangle skeins
that lie within the lap. But now all France
is one great skein, beyond the reach of fingers.
Her heart demands a final desperate sortie,
a rallying about the lilied banner,
defiance and a horse, not this long death.
But in the sultry shadow of disaster
in her last palace, among her huddled ladies,
the queen embroiders through the endless hours.

Montezuma's Song

Had they not come in the Year of the Morning Star
out of the east and the sea,
had they not been bearded with pallid faces,
had he not worn a helmet like the helmet of the god of
    war
the throne had stood, the gods
had still stood in
their places.

I remember how my heart beat as I heard the news of
    their coming
and saw the pictures the bearers brought of their horses
    and their turreted ships.
I held the helmet between my hands as the kneeling
    messengers babbled
of their haughty speech
and the beards dark
and curling about
their lips.

What did the priests say: "Where is the white Quetzal-
    coatl
and when shall he come?
The land is a woman who has slain
her children and bears no more." Their prophecies always

beat in my ears like the
cold numbing fall of
the rain.

And I sat uncertain, when I should have sent forth and
    killed them,
and I waited for omens when omen enough was my will,
and I exchanged greetings with them, and called
their leaders my brothers
while the prophecies dulled
my mind and I was
uncertain still.

Where are my palaces, where are my pleasant gardens,
where are my wives and my daughters, gentle and tall?
What gods still sit on their thrones,
in shrines as yet unpolluted?
Does any watchman blow
the conch of war
from the wall?

I have let the kingdom fall like a pot from my nerveless
    fingers
to break on the ground: the water of might is spilled,
no hand shall gather it up,
for the insatiable earth is thirsty,
the flower grows not
again after the root
is killed.

They sent me up to the roof to quiet the people.

The people stoned me with stones, who am god and
   priest and king.
Now the Spaniards bind up my wounds,
but I have again unbound them
that my blood may moisten
the ground so the Lady
Earth may sing—

> *"Montezuma is dead.*
>   *Let him be forgotten.*
> *He was a proud tree*
>   *but the wood was rotten.*
> *He was a tall spear*
>   *that missed its mark.*
> *He was a high torch*
>   *that died in the dark."*

Where Are the
Daughters of Montezuma?

Where are the daughters of Montezuma?
Where are the flowers that grew by his wall?
Time like a wind has scattered the blossoms,
the river moves on and returns not at all.
Lost like birds which a shout has frightened,
gone like deer when the arrow flies,
the daughters of kings have fled into hiding
nothing tells of their birth but their telltale eyes.
They were jewels of jade strung on a necklace,
the cord has been broken, and scatter they must,
to be lost is their hope, for their beauty and luster
are only safe in the keeping of dust.

Return

Sometimes the moment comes for the return,
the drawing-back-again into the known:
the remembered room, the loved face, the accepted idea.
Even Ulysses knew that secret magnet
which through the years of sea and island wanderings
    gave him no rest.
Nymphs were not beautiful enough,
nor the salt waves
so bright and daunting as to bar the way.
The Circe islands might delay his coming
but could not stop him. The loud-voiced gulls
in vain cried Freedom on the veering winds.
The sirens sang to deaf ears, even Polyphemus,
the stupid, lovesick, man-devouring shepherd,
had not the wits in his thick ogre's skull
to match Ulysses' homeward-trending will.
There comes the time for each and every one
to be Ulysses. Somewhere the tapestry
is woven and unwoven. Somewhere the dog
lies blind and listening in the familiar sun.